s

All football facts correct at time of going to press
ISBN: 1 85386 169 3
© Fleetway Publications 1990

£3.95

ROY of the ROVERS

RACEY'S RAIDERS, VERSUS SOAPS UNITED... YET ANOTHER LIGHT-HEARTED GAME IN SUPPORT OF ROY'S PERSONAL CHILDREN'S CHARITY 'RACE-AID'...

...BEAUTIFUL DUMMY! RACEY'S WRONG-FOOTED THE SOAPS' DEFENCE!

HE'S SET UP A SITTER FOR *GREG WOOTTEN*!

OOOOOHHHHHH!

ROY OFTEN USED THESE GAMES TO GIVE PROMISING PLAYERS A TRIAL...

...YOU CAN TELL THAT GREG WOOTTEN IS THE BROTHER OF NOBBY WOOTTEN, THE ROVERS' RIGHT BACK!

HE LOOKS PRETTY IMPRESSIVE! QUITE A FAVOURITE WITH THE CROWD, TOO!

4

...BUT IT WAS *WASTED EFFORT!* GREG HAD PLENTY OF TIME TO PULL THE BALL DOWN, AND PICK HIS SPOT! I'M AFRAID HE *FANCIES HIMSELF*, NOBBY..!

BUT—!

YOUR BROTHER JUST ISN'T MELCHESTER MATERIAL...NOT YET, ANYWAY! SORRY, NOB...

...I'LL LEAVE YOU TO BREAK THE DISAPPOINTING NEWS!

LATER...

...HE THINKS I'M *TOO FLASHY?* HE ISN'T EVEN GOING TO GIVE ME AN EXTENDED TRIAL?

I TRIED, GREG! LOOK, MAYBE IF YOU DID WELL AGAINST US FOR LENFIELD..!

I'LL DO MORE THAN THAT! HEY, YOU LOT... I ALWAYS THOUGHT ROY RACE WAS AN EXPERT JUDGE OF TALENT!

GREG!

ROY HAD BEEN GIVING AN INTERVIEW TO LOCAL RADIO ABOUT THE CHARITY GAME...

...I THOUGHT BRITISH FOOTBALL *NEEDED* A BIT OF SKILL, AND FLAIR! WELL, I'M GOING TO PROVE THAT HE'S *TOTALLY WRONG* ABOUT ME ...NEXT SATURDAY...*IN FRONT OF FIFTY THOUSAND PEOPLE!*

ER...SORRY ABOUT THAT, BOSS! IT'S JUST THAT GREG HAS ALWAYS DREAMED ABOUT PLAYING FOR THE ROVERS! HE'S SHATTERED!

THAT'S PUTTING IT MILDLY. THE MEDIA WILL HAVE A FIELD DAY WITH THAT LITTLE OUTBURST!

ROY WAS RIGHT!

SPORTS

"I'LL PUT GOALS WHERE MY MOUTH IS" — WOOTTEN!

DAILY GLOBE

CHARITY MATCH SENSATION!

★ MELCHESTER ECHO ★

LENFIELD ACE THROWS DOWN THE GAUNTLET!

THE CONTROVERSY SPREAD TO THE MELCHESTER PLAYER-MANAGER'S HOME...

POOR NOBBY! THIS MUST ALL BE VERY UNSETTLING FOR HIM, ROY!

ARE YOU SUGGESTING THAT I SHOULD DROP HIM FROM THE CUP-TIE SQUAD?

NO WAY... NOBBY'S A PROFESSIONAL! HE'LL COPE WITH THE SITUATION!

THAT'S RIGHT, MY SON!

...COP THAT, LENFIELD!

HA! HA! HAAAAA!

MATCH DAY...

...THIS MAY NOT BE THE WALK-OVER FOR ROVERS THAT EVERYONE IS EXPECTING!

NOT WITH GREG WOOTTEN STILL SHOOTING HIS MOUTH OFF..!

HE PLAYS WIDE DOWN THE LEFT FOR LENFIELD, SO NOBBY WILL BE MARKING HIM!

COULD BE VERY, VERY INTERESTING...!

HILLS BREAD

A FEW MOMENTS AFTER THE KICK-OFF...

TOWN ARE BRINGING YOUNG GREGORY MORE AND MORE INTO THE GAME!

FORGET THE *BROTHERLY LOVE*, NOBBY ...*NAIL HIM!*

GOOD GRIEF! THAT TACKLE WOULDN'T HAVE NAILED A FEATHER DUSTER!

UU-UUNNG!

GREG WENT CLEAN *THROUGH* HIM!

THE MELCHESTER DEFENDERS WERE AS STUNNED AS THE FANS...AND BEFORE THEY COULD RECOVER...

...USEFUL CROSS ...AND *IT'S THERE!*

ROVERS WERE ALL OVER THE PLACE!

BUT...

...*TERRIBLE* HEADER! IT'S SKIDDED OFF THE BACK OF HIS NUT!

AA-AACH!

GREG WOOTTEN'S GOT A FREE BALL...!

AS LENFIELD CONTINUED TO PUT PRESSURE ON NOBBY WOOTTEN...

...NO PROBLEM HERE! NOBBY'S GOT ALL THE TIME IN THE WORLD...!

GET *IN* THERE!

TWO-NIL TO LENFIELD! THIS IS CRAZY..!

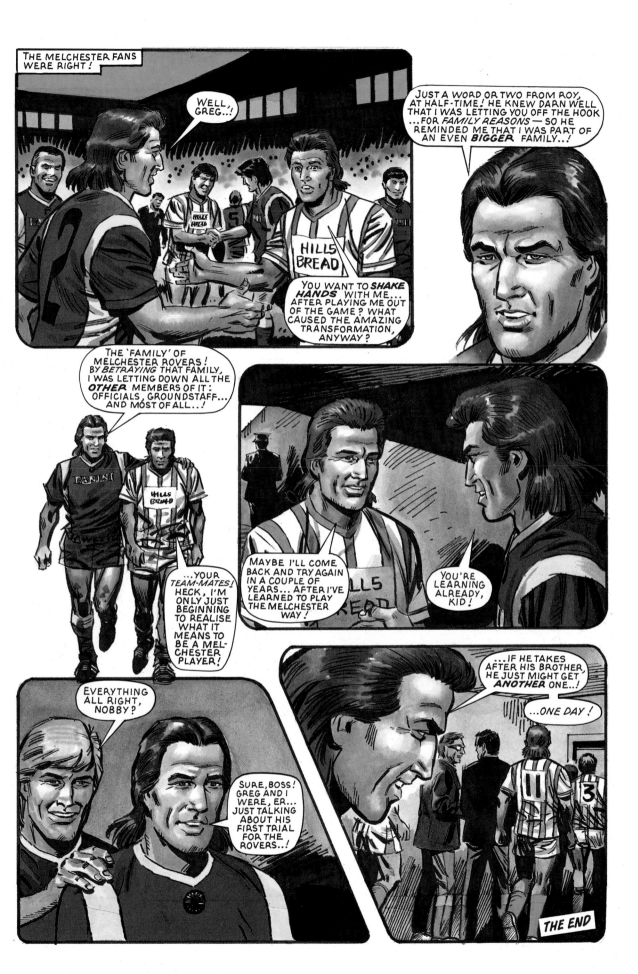

11

MASTER CL

Peter Shilton...40 years young and still England's number one.

There is a lot of talent on today's goalkeeping scene. Roy takes a look at some of the best...

12

ASS

As a striker, nobody appreciates the value of a top-class goalkeeper more than me and I am surprised that it was not until Crystal Palace bought Nigel Martyn from Bristol Rovers in 1989 that a club had paid £1 million for a goalkeeper.

I cannot understand why clubs seem to think goalkeepers are less valuable than strikers, midfielders or defenders.

Managers freely admit that a really good goalkeeper can be worth up to 12 points a season to them yet so often they value the men between the sticks at a fraction of the fee paid for an outfield player.

Without mentioning any names, the prices paid for certain players these days are sky-high yet Peter Shilton, in my book just about the greatest goalkeeper of modern times, has never commanded a fee of more than £340,000.

Shilts, with his ability to stop a shot that has "goal" written all over it and break a striker's heart, must have won dozens of games for his clubs (and England) throughout his career.

Peter made his debut in League football before most of you were born – in 1966 for Leicester around the time England were winning the World Cup.

Since then, he's played for Stoke, Nottingham Forest, Southampton and Derby with distinction. In my view, Peter is a million pound goalkeeper whatever his transfer fees may have been..

People have been talking about Shilton's successor in the England team for years but aged 40, he was still in brilliant form as England qualified for the 1990 World Cup Finals.

It is also remarkable to think how many caps Peter would have had if Ray Clemence had not been chosen ahead of Shilts between 1974 and 1979 when Peter won only four caps. If Peter had been the regular choice then, he would have won more than 150 caps by now.

However, even Shilts can't go on forever and I wonder who will eventually wear the England jersey he has filled with such distinction?

The candidates seen to be (in no particular order), Nigel Martyn, Chris Woods, Dave Beasant and David Seaman.

I like what I've seen of Nigel who certainly found himself a busy goalkeeper when he moved

Dave Beasant's famous penalty save from Liverpool's John Aldridge, when Wimbledon won the 1988 FA Cup.

13

Glasgow Rangers' goalie Chris Woods has fought back from injury and illness.

Britain's first £1 million 'keeper...Crystal Palace's Nigel Martyn.

Pat Bonner of Celtic — a hero in Ireland and Scotland.

from Bristol Rovers to Palace.

He had played only two full seasons in the lower division with Rovers before Palace snapped him up and Nigel was plunged straight into a battle against relegation as the Londoners fought to remain in the First Division.

Beasant made his name as a goalkeeper-sweeper at Wimbledon. At times he seemed to have the ball OUTSIDE of his penalty area more then INSIDE it!

But he was so confident in his ability that he was not afraid to dribble upfield before releasing one of his huge cannonball-like kicks to his forwards.

Most important, Dave is a commanding goalkeeper inside his area. His huge frame enables him to dictate what goes on near his goal.

Dave's most memorable moment came in the 1988 FA Cup Final when he saved a penalty from Liverpool's John Aldridge as Wimbledon won the FA Cup 1–0. Dave is the only goalkeeper to captain an FA Cup-winning team but left the Wombles for Newcastle soon after the Wembley triumph.

His transfer to Newcastle didn't really work out but since returning to London with Chelsea, "Lurch" has won promotion to the England squad.

I feel sorry for Chris Woods. For just about any other country, the Glasgow Rangers goalkeeper would be a regular in the national side.

Chris has suffered from "Shiltonitis" and has had to remain in Peter's shadow. But Chris's attitude has been excellent and despite setbacks with illness and injury, he has maintained his position as England's second Number One.

Chris at least holds a record that even Shilts cannot claim. The British record for keeping a clean sheet for the longest time is 1,196 minutes by Chris who was unbeaten from November 26th,

Nottingham Forest's Steve Sutton is one of the most underrated goalkeepers in the League.

1986 until January 31st, 1987.

The record was broken in dramatic style by Adrian Sprott's 70th minute goal for Hamilton in their shock 1–0 Scottish Cup win over mighty Rangers.

David Seaman played for Leeds, Peterborough and Birmingham before joining Queens Park Rangers in a £250,000 deal in 1986. What a shrewd piece of business that was by Rangers because David was rated in the £1 million bracket when Arsenal were first reported to be interested in him in 1989.

Seaman is one of those no-nonsense goalkeepers who may not be spectacular, but he gets the job done without fuss.

Scottish goalkeepers have often come under fire from English critics – with good old Jimmy Greaves leading the way! – but Jim Leighton has surely proved that he is above all the jokes Greavsie cracks.

Jim had a marvellous career with Aberdeen who, under Alex Ferguson, won just about everything in sight as the dynamic Dons dominated Scottish football.

Fergie took Jim to Manchester United in 1988 and while the Reds' fortunes have been mixed, the Old Trafford fans took to the goalkeeper immediately.

One of the best shot-stoppers in the First Division is Arsenal's John Lukic. John doesn't always seem to get the credit he deserves at Highbury but whenever I see him I'm impressed by the way he invariably seems to save shots...one way or the other.

Just as a striker can score a goal with a mis-hit shot, goalkeepers can make seemingly lucky saves with their legs. But they all count! If I score the winner with a 30-yard shot it is still only one goal...the same as if the ball goes past the goalkeeper off my shin!

Pat Bonner made his debut for Celtic in 1978 but it is only in the past few years that he has been

QPR's David Seaman is a safe goalkeeper who gets his job done without frills.

recognised as a top-class goalkeeper.

He has been part of the Republic of Ireland's rise in world football. Ireland's defensive record has been so good under Jack Charlton, who took over as manager in 1986, that Pat has picked the ball out of his net probably fewer times than just about any other regular international goalkeeper in Europe in the past four years.

I feel a little sorry for Everton's Neville Southall. Many reckon he's the best goalkeeper in the world but because Wales are in the international doldrums, Nev hasn't had the chance to display his many talents at the highest level.

We've seen a few foreign goalkeepers make their mark in the Football League but perhaps the best is Erik Thorstvedt of Spurs.

The Norwegian had the worst possible start to his career in English soccer by conceding a soft goal in a live television game on his debut in 1988-89 against Nottingham Forest.

But he showed his character and was voted Player of the Year at White Hart Lane in 1989.

I suppose Bruce Grobbelaar qualifies as an overseas goalkeeper as he was born in South Africa but he's been part of the Liverpool team since 1981 and is definitely an honorary Merseysider!

Bruce always seems to have a smile on his face and I like to see players enjoying their work.

His style is individual and he'd own up to the odd blunder. But he has made many, many more stunning saves than he's made errors and nobody keeps his place at Liverpool for years unless he is an outstanding player...which Bruce certainly is.

There are many more solid goalkeepers who do a fine job for their clubs week-in, week-out without grabbing the headlines.

Men such as Steve Ogrizovic of Coventry, Steve Sutton of Nottingham Forest, Tim Flowers of Southampton, Bryan Gunn of Norwich and others up and down the League.

The Football League record for keeping a clean sheet is held by Steve Death of Reading between March 24th and August 18th, 1979. Steve's run was ended in the opening match of 1979/80 season by...an own-goal by Reading full-back Stewart Henderson who deflected the ball past his own goalkeeper in the first half.

Please excuse me, now – I have some goals to score. I hope!

ACTION EXTRA

Clive Allen
Manchester City

Throughout his career with QPR (twice), Arsenal, Crystal Palace, Spurs, Bordeaux and Manchester City, Clive Allen has averaged a goal every other game...a strike rate every forward would be proud of.

18

IT'S THERE!

GROUNDWOOD ARE IN THE FINAL NOW! THEY'VE GOT TO BE!

AND BILLY DANE SET IT UP!

FIVE MINUTES LATER...

HOPE MINE'S A HORROR-FILM VIDEO!

WELL PLAYED, LADS! I'VE GOT A *PRESENT* FOR YOU!

COULD BE! LIKE YOU SCORING AN OWN-GOAL!

A NEW STRIP FOR EVERYONE FOR NEXT WEEK'S FINAL! FROM OUR SPONSORS! SOCKS, SHORTS, SHIRTS AND BOOTS!

GREAT!

FOOTA SPORTSWEAR LOOK AFTER US, DON'T THEY?

I DON'T WANT TO WEAR THESE! I WANT MY OWN OLD BOOTS!

YOU'VE *GOT* TO, BILLY!

ESPECIALLY YOU! YOU'RE THE *CAPTAIN*!

THE FOOTA SPORTSWEAR PEOPLE WOULD NOTICE THE *DIFFERENCE*, WOULDN'T THEY?

YOU'VE GOT TO BE *FAIR*! FOOTA HAVE LAID IT ALL ON ...AND THE *WINNING* TEAM GETS A HUNDRED QUID FOR THEIR SPORTS FUND!

At home...

I'LL BE *USELESS* IF I WEAR THOSE NEW BOOTS! STILL, I SUPPOSE I COULD GET SOME PRACTICE BEFORE NEXT WEEK. I *MIGHT* BE ABLE TO PLAY IN 'EM! THEY LOOK ALL RIGHT...

BILLY WENT UP TO THE REC...

WANT TO JOIN IN, BILLY? WE'RE ONLY HAVING A KICK-AROUND!

YEAH, THANKS.

19

THEY *FEEL* COMFORTABLE ENOUGH! I'LL TRY A LONG PASS OUT TO THAT KID ON THE FAR SIDE...

OH, HECK! THAT'S NO GOOD!

WHADDYA *DOING*?

WAS THAT SUPPOSED TO BE A *PASS*?

THEN...

YOUR BALL, BILLY! HAVE A GO!

ALL THE TIME IN THE WORLD TO SHOOT!

FLAMING HECK! DANE'S IN THE FOOTA CUP FINAL, TOO!

HE'LL HAVE TO DO BETTER THAN *THAT*!

RUBBISH!

I CAN'T *PASS* AND I CAN'T *SHOOT*!

AND...

EASY!

AND I CAN'T *DRIBBLE*, EITHER!

NEXT DAY AT SCHOOL...

TRIED OUT YOUR NEW BOOTS, BILLY?

HOW'D YOU GET ON?

ROTTEN! I'D BETTER NOT PLAY IN THE FINAL. I'LL TELL MR. GRANT I'M INJURED...

I'M USELESS IN THOSE NEW BOOTS! I CAN'T DO A THING RIGHT...

DON'T BE DAFT! YOU'VE *GOT* TO PLAY!

IT'S NOT THE *BOOTS*, BILLY! IT'S *YOU*! YOU'RE NERVOUS, THAT'S ALL!

Mo Johnston stunned
Scottish football
when he joined
Rangers in 1989 and
soon showed that
Celtic's loss was very
much their rivals'
gain.

JOY

Chris Waddle has developed into one of the most complete forwards in Europe since his £4.25 million transfer from Tottenham to Marseille.

BOYS!

JOY BOYS!

RIGHT
Two of Europe's top stars in action...Gary Lineker of Tottenham and England – and Frank Rijkaard of AC Milan and Holland. Lineker returned to English football from Barcelona in 1989 and quickly showed he had lost none of the skills that had made him such a favourite with Leicester and Everton fans before his move to Spain.

BELOW
A goal-maker and a goal-taker...Peter Beardsley of Liverpool, one of the most unselfish players in England.

FAR RIGHT
Paul Gascoigne, the popular Spurs and England midfielder, is known simply as Gazza to his many fans. Perhaps Dazzler would be just as appropriate for a player who has the sort of skills that made him worth £2 million when he joined Spurs from Newcastle. He can pass over seemingly any distance and find a team-mate while his dribbling ability leaves defenders tackling his shadow.

SPOT THE DIFFERENCE

BULLY FOR

US!

*T*he Tipton Terrier...Raging Bull...call him what you want, but there is no denying that Steve Bull has been just about the most prolific goalscorer in the League over the past four years. He played only four League games for West Brom before joining Wolves for £60,000 in 1986/87 and since then it's been goals all the way. When Wolves win, fans ask how many goals Bull scored, not IF he scored. Steve has proved that he can not only score goals in the lower divisions, but also at international level. In 1989 he was on the mark for England's Under-21's, the B team and the full national side. On the opposite page Steve is challenged by Paul McGrath of Aston Villa while above Bully shows his skills for England against Denmark.

BYRD of PARADISE HILL

HAMPTON ORIENT WERE WELL ON THEIR WAY TO A WIN AGAINST TOUGH TROWTOWN UNITED ... *THANKS MAINLY TO RICHARD BYRD...*

COME ON, DICKY BYRD! LET'S HAVE ONE MORE FOR ORIENT!

BYRD'S ALWAYS GOOD! BUT TODAY HE'S PLAYING A SCORCHER OF A GAME!

...AND ALSO TO ORIENT'S NEW £400,000 WINGER, FRANK SMALES...

IT'S GONE TO SMALES!

LOOK AT HIM GO!

TOGETHER, BYRD AND SMALES FORMED A PARTNERSHIP WHICH HAD TROWTOWN STAGGERING...

HE'S PASSED IT BACK... RIGHT BETWEEN TROWTOWN'S DEFENDERS!

NOW, BYRD! *NOW!*

OF ALL THE YELLING ORIENT SUPPORTERS, NONE YELLED MORE LOUDLY THAN A BUNCH OF TOUGH-LOOKING TEENAGERS FROM PARADISE HILL COMPREHENSIVE SCHOOL...

GO IT, GUV!

GAWW! WHAT A GAME! IN THE NET WITH IT, DICKIE!

ONE MORE FOR OLD PARADISE HILL, SIR!

FOR, IN ADDITION TO BEING THE STAR PLAYER OF HAMPTON ORIENT, RICHARD BYRD WAS ALSO *SPORTS MASTER* AT PARADISE HILL SCHOOL...

LOOK AT 'EM! THEY GOT THE BALL GOIN' BACK AND FORWARDS LIKE PERISHIN' *PING-PONG*!

I... I CAN'T FLIPPIN' WELL SEE! GET *OUT* OF IT, YA BIG GORILLA!

CALL ME *GORILLA* AGAIN, MATE... AND I'LL BELT YOU RIGHT OUT OF THIS FLIPPIN' STADIUM!

THE TROWTOWN GOALIE HAD EXPECTED FRANK SMALES TO TRY TO SCORE...

IT'S THERE! HOOO-RAAYY! ORIENT!

THE GOALIE HARDLY SAW WHERE IT CAME FROM!

THE KIDS FROM PARADISE HILL RUSHED FOR THE EXITS AS THE WHISTLE SOUNDED A FOUR-NIL WIN FOR HAMPTON...

LET'S GET OUT AND BOOT A BALL ABOUT. I'M ALL INSPIRED!

YEAH! THAT DICKY BYRD AND FRANK SMALES PASS IS SOMETHING I'D LIKE TO TRY!

IN THE CHANGING ROOM...

YOU'RE A SCHOOL TEACHER, DICKY. I'VE DECIDED TO SEND MY KID BROTHER HAL TO WINCHTON COLLEGE! WHAT DO YOU THINK?

PHEW!! THINK IT'S GOING TO COST YOU *A PACKET*, FRANK! WINCHTON'S ONE OF THE MOST EXPENSIVE SCHOOLS IN THE COUNTRY! VERY LA-DI-DA, TOO!

EVER SINCE I STARTED TO EARN GOOD MONEY AT SOCCER I'VE TRIED TO GIVE HAL THE BEST HE CAN GET! HE'S A GOOD KID. A BIT COCKY, BUT...

A **LOT** OF NICE KIDS CAN BE PRETTY COCKY AT TIMES. I KNOW A WHOLE DARNED SCHOOL FULL OF KIDS LIKE THAT... **MY** SCHOOL!

34

BEFORE PARADISE HILL COULD RETALIATE, THE WHISTLE BLEW FOR HALF-TIME...

SORRY ABOUT THAT!

THINK NOTHING OF IT, MATE! I'D HAVE DONE IT TO YOU, IF I'D 'AD THE CHANCE!

PHEEP!

THE WINCHTON HEADMASTER WAS PLEASED...

AGGRESSIVENESS! THAT'S WHAT MY LADS WERE LACKING. BUT THEY'RE LEARNING ABOUT IT... FROM YOUR BOYS, MR. BYRD!

AND MY LADS ARE LEARNING THAT TOUGH TACTICS ALONE WON'T GET THEM ANYWHERE!

WITH FIVE MINUTES LEFT, THE SCORE WAS STILL THE SAME.

LOOK OUT, HAL! THEY'RE COMING AT YOU BOTH WAYS!

WINCHTON! WINCHTON!

SUDDENLY FLASH HARRIS LEAPT ASIDE AND...

NOW, FLASH... MOVE!

FLASH WAS COVERING UP ACE BAMPSTER! 'ERE 'E COMES!

FOR A MOMENT, HAL SMALES' EYES SWUNG TO FOLLOW FLASH HARRIS ... AND IN THAT MOMENT...

THEY TRICKED HIM! PARADISE HILL HAVE GOT THE BALL!

TAKE IT UP, ACE! WE'RE RIGHT WITH YOU, MATE!

VALIANTLY, A WINCHTON HALF-BACK TACKLED, BUT...

HAL SMALES IS TRYING TO GET HIM!

TO YOU, CURLY!

THE WINCHTON BACKS ARE UP TOO FAR! HE'S GOT A CLEAR RUN AT THE GOAL!

WO
BEA

*F*ew would argue that Diego Maradona is the best footballer in the world. He has proved this with his club, Napoli, and his country, Argentina, many times. Here we take a closer look at Magnificent Maradona and some other leading stars of world football.

ABOVE
Enzo Francescoli...the Uruguayan star midfield man who is a team-mate of Chris Waddle in France with Marseille. Uruguay have a reputation of playing hard, uncompromising football but this must not overshadow the skills of players such as Francescoli.

RIGHT
Alain Geiger of Switzerland (dark strip) and Czechoslovakia's Michal Bilek in action during a 1990 World Cup qualifying tie in Berne which the Czechs won 1–0.

RLD ERS

TOP RIGHT
Johnny Ekstroem, the Sweden striker and one of the most feared forwards in Europe.

RIGHT
Probably the most famous footballer in the world...Diego Maradona, captain of Argentina, seen here being tackled by Belgium's Eric Gerets.

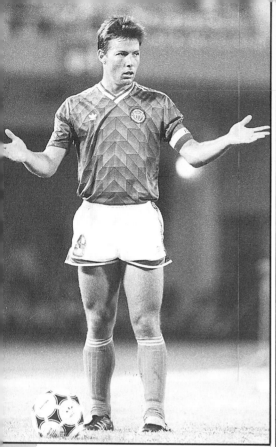

Rick Davis is reckoned to be the best player ever produced by the United States of America, World Cup finalists in 1990.

Carlos Valderrama, the brilliant Colombian forward who is a former South American Footballer of the Year.

A great defender meets a great striker...Italy's Giuseppe Bergomi (left) tussles with Holland's Marco Van Basten.

Scotland midfielder Roy Aitken left Celtic to sign for Newcastle for £500,000 six months before the 1990 World Cup Finals.

Alexander Zavarov, a highly skilled midfielder from the Soviet Union who joined Juventus when Ian Rush re-signed for Liverpool.

Safat Susic, one of the many talented players of Yugoslavia.

Antoine Joseph Bell, the Cameroon goalkeeper who helped the Africans to reach the World Cup finals for the second time in 1990.

Romario, the Brazil striker, is closely marked by Argentina's Oscar Ruggeri, who seems to come out on top on this occasion.

ABOVE
Rodion Camataru, the Romanian striker, has been one of the most regular marksmen in Europe in recent years.

44

ABOVE
Ray Houghton plays in England for Liverpool but at international level is a star for Republic of Ireland.

ABOVE
Juergen Kilnsmann has emerged as West Germany's top striker since the 1988 European Championship Finals.

ABOVE
They call him the Vulture...Emilio Butragueno, the brilliant Real Madrid and Spain centre-forward.

HARD MEN!

Every successful team must have one...they sometimes make the headlines for the wrong reasons but soccer's hard men put a bite into football. When the going gets tough, the tough get going and the Soccer Sampsons certainly make their presence felt. Take Vinny Jones, for instance.

The one-time hod carrier was given his chance in League football by Dave Bassett, then manager of Wimbledon and while Vinny won as many enemies as friends, he proved to be a great guy to have on your side. So great, in fact, that Leeds were prepared to pay £650,000 for the Jones boy in the summer of 1989 to supplement their bid for promotion to the First Division. The picture on the right sums up Vinny. The shaved head (well, almost all shaved!), the stern appearance...sweat and mud on his kit. Vinny is the first to admit he doesn't have the close skills of, say, Gordon Strachan. But someone has to win the ball for the ball-players to show their ability. At Leeds, more often than not, it's Vinny who is the winner.

ABOVE
Stuart Pearce, the Nottingham Forest left-back and skipper, gives wingers a hard time.

RIGHT
Jimmy Case, the Southampton captain, has the ability to win the ball and use it well.

HARD MEN!

When Liverpool and England midfielder Steve McMahon tackles...opponents stay tackled!

ACTION EXTRA

David Platt
Aston Villa

Manchester United allowed David to move to Crewe, but he joined Villa in 1987 and is now in the £2 million class. David made his full international debut in 1989/90.

49

RICK STEWART WAS THE BRILLIANT YOUNG GOALKEEPER OF TYNEFIELD CITY'S YOUTH TEAM, AND HE PLAYED MANY OUTSTANDING GAMES FOR HIS CLUB...

GENTLEMEN, IT'S NO GOOD BEATING ABOUT THE BUSH, THE FACE OF FOOTBALL IN THIS COUNTRY IS *TARNISHED*. WE NEED A NEW IMAGE AFTER SOME OF THE POOR PUBLICITY WE'VE HAD.

HAS ANYONE GOT ANY BRIGHT IDEAS?

PUBLICITY MAN BOBBY BURGESS JUMPED TO HIS FEET...

YES, SIR — I HAVE! I THINK WE SHOULD EMBARK ON A PUBLIC RELATIONS CAMPAIGN THAT WILL KNOCK THE PUBLIC FOR *SIX!*

WHAT MIGHT THAT BE?

YOU SAID THE FACE OF FOOTBALL IS TARNISHED. THEN I SAY WE SHOULD SUPPLY THE GAME WITH A *NEW FACE*. FIND A YOUNGSTER WITH THE PERFECT IMAGE!

THEY JUMPED AT IT. THE ONLY PROBLEM I'VE GOT NOW IS THAT IT'S GOING TO BE *MY* JOB TO FIND THE FACE!

IT WAS SATURDAY. BOBBY BURGESS'S ROUTE TOOK HIM THROUGH TYNEFIELD PARK...

THERE'S A GAME GOING ON. I MIGHT AS WELL TAKE A LOOK.

WHO'S PLAYING, PAL?

TYNEFIELD YOUTH TEAM AGAINST SELSDON UNITED YOUTH. NO SCORE YET. GOOD GAME THOUGH.

AT THAT MOMENT...

A LOVELY BALL INTO SPACE.

THERE'S A CHANCE ON HERE. HE'S GOT PLENTY OF SPACE TO SHOOT...

THE BALL WAS HIT LIKE A ROCKET...

IT'S A GOAL! GOING IN THE TOP CORNER...

BUT...

NO! THE REF'S NOT GIVEN IT! HE'S POINTING FOR A GOAL-KICK!

BUT THE BALL WENT OVER THE LINE. IT WAS A GOAL!

EXCUSE ME, REF. THEY'RE RIGHT. IT WAS A GOAL. THE NETTING HAS COME UNCLIPPED FROM THE UPRIGHT. THE BALL WENT STRAIGHT THROUGH.

THE REF'S CHANGED HIS MIND. HE'S GIVEN IT AFTER ALL.

IT WAS DOWN TO THEIR 'KEEPER.

WHAT A SPORTSMAN!

THANK YOU, GOALKEEPER. I WISH THERE WERE MORE PLAYERS LIKE YOU.

THAT'S HIM! THAT'S MY BOY! THE NEW FACE OF FOOTBALL! I'VE FOUND HIM AT MY FIRST ATTEMPT!

BOBBY BURGESS WAS A FAST TALKER...

...AND THAT'S IT, RICK. IN MY VIEW, YOU'RE THE PERFECT CHOICE. YOU'LL GET PAID ALL EXPENSES, AND WE'LL DONATE £10,000 TO A CHARITY OF YOUR CHOICE.

OKAY, I'LL DO IT!

THAT'S IT—GOOD. JUST THINK OF THE CAMERA AS TEN MILLION PEOPLE, AND YOU'RE SMILING AT EVERY SINGLE ONE OF THEM!

EVERYONE IN THE COUNTRY WILL KNOW YOUR FACE WHEN WE'VE FINISHED, RICK!

YOU'LL BE AS FAMOUS AS THE STARS OF "NEIGHBOURS"!

YOU HAVE SUCH A *SWEET* FACE, MISTER STEWART. SO APPEALING. I JUST *KNOW* ALL THE READERS OF MY MAGAZINE WILL WANT TO MOTHER YOU.

AHEM! HOW—ER—NICE!

THE HIGH-POWERED PUBLICITY OPERATION SWUNG SMOOTHLY INTO ACTION. IT WAS ONLY WEEKS BEFORE...

WOW! IT'S *ME*! GIANT SIZE!

THE PERFECT FACE OF FOOTBALL! THE GAME FOR ALL THE FAMILY TO WATCH!

AND JUST AROUND THE CORNER...

SUPPORT YOUR LOCAL FOOTBALL CLUB. BE HAPPY!

THERE I AM AGAIN!

AND HERE IS RICK STEWART OF TYNEFIELD CITY, ON WHOM OUR PUBLICITY CAMPAIGN IS BASED. HE IS THE *FACE OF FOOTBALL* WE WANT TO PORTRAY IN THE MEDIA.

THE ROUND OF PRESS CONFERENCES, COCKTAIL PARTIES AND PRESENTATIONS SEEMED TO GO ON... AND ON...

HOW MANY MORE OF THESE FUNCTIONS HAVE I GOT TO ATTEND, MISTER BURGESS?

WE'RE ALMOST THROUGH, RICK. BUT IT'S *WORKING*. EVERYONE'S TALKING ABOUT YOU... AS I SAID THEY WOULD.

GOOD. IT'S THE BIG GAME AGAINST BRADPORT ON SATURDAY. I'VE NOT BEEN TO BED BEFORE MIDNIGHT ANY NIGHT THIS WEEK AND I'M FEELING *SHATTERED!*

WHEN SATURDAY CAME...

SOMETHING THE MATTER, RICK? YOU DON'T SEEM YOUR USUAL LIVELY SELF.

I CAN HARDLY KEEP MY EYES OPEN, JOHN, I'M SO TIRED.

TIRED, EH? I'VE GOT THE PERFECT ANSWER FOR YOU, GLAMOUR BOY!

...AN ICE-COLD SHOWER! *IN* YOU GO, GOAL-KEEPER!

YAAAAAAHHHHHHHH!

I C-CAN'T STOP SH-*SHIVERING* ...BUT AT LEAST IT'S WOKEN ME UP!

RICK WAS IN ACTION THROUGHOUT THE FIRST HALF...

SAAAAVED GOALKEEPER!

HE HAD TO BE QUICK TO KEEP THAT ONE OUT!

JUST OVER THE BAR!

...AND EVEN QUICKER TO GRAB THAT!

THERE WAS NO SCORE AT THE INTERVAL...

NO, JOHN! YOU'VE GOT THAT GLINT IN YOUR EYE! NO...

YES, RICK! YOU'RE LOOKING TIRED AGAIN. GET THAT GEAR OFF...

UNDER YOU GO, AGAIN! WE'VE GOT TO KEEP YOU WIDE AWAKE AND ON YOUR TOES IF WE'RE TO WIN THIS MATCH!

EEEEEEK! IT—IT'S F-F-F-FREEZING!

THE COLD SHOWER DID THE TRICK AGAIN.

A SENSATIONAL SAVE BY THE GOAL-KEEPER!

HE'S UNBEATABLE!

AS THE MATCH NEARED ITS CLOSE...

YOUR BALL, RICK! WAKE UP!

HUH? OH —RIGHT!

r.
gic!

When John Barnes arrived in England from Jamaica as a teenager, it was his dream to become a professional footballer. He could not – even in his wildest dreams – have believed he would be so successful. He established himself as one of the most exciting and effective wingers in the First Division with Watford but since joining Liverpool his career has really taken off. He seems to have magic in his boots...as opponents of the Merseysiders and England would testify!

ALL-ROUND EXPERT QUIZ

Paul Goddard

GOAL
Defence
Midfield
Attack

1. MARK HUGHES, STEVE ARCHIBALD and GARY LINEKER have all played for the same continental team. Can you name the club?
   ANSWER _____

2. You are taking the kick-off at the start of a match. In which direction must the ball travel?
   ANSWER _____

3. Which club did Kevin Drinkell play for before he moved to Rangers? Was it Coventry, Norwich or West Ham?
   ANSWER _____

4. YONT ETTOCE. Unscramble the name of an English sharp-shooter.
   ANSWER _____

5. Lee Chapman used to play for Arsenal. True or false?
   ANSWER _____

6. Goddard and Saunders may sound like a comic double act, but it was no laughing matter for opposition defences when this deadly duo came together. At which club did they strike up a partnership? Was it Derby, Millwall or Southampton?
   ANSWER _____

7. Every striker has got to know this . . . how many goals in a hat-trick?
   ANSWER _____

8. Two forwards at Spurs sharing the same name. They're Walsh and Stewart. What is the shared first name?
   ANSWER _____

9. Who am I? I started with Celtic, then moved to Arsenal. After four seasons with The Gunners I moved on to Aberdeen. I'm a Scottish international.
   ANSWER _____

10. Which star England forward became a player/manager with QPR at Christmas time in 1988?
    ANSWER _____

11. Kenny Dalglish is another great player/manager. He became the boss at Liverpool but which club did he move from? Was it Celtic, Rangers or Sunderland?
    ANSWER _____

12. The top scorer in the 1986 World Cup final stages was an Englishman. Can you name him?
    ANSWER _____

ANSWERS

1 Barcelona, 2 Forwards, 3 Norwich, 4 Tony Cottee, 5 True, 6 Derby, 7 Three, 8 Paul, 9 Charlie Nicholas, 10 Trevor Francis, 11 Celtic, 12 Gary Lineker.

TOP SCORE 12
MY SCORE _____

RATINGS
TOTAL SCORE
MY SCORE   48
_____

40 and above Congratulations. You are an ALL-ROUND EXPERT. You are tip-top in all areas of the pitch.

33 to 39 A very good display. Good all-round showing.

26 to 32 A fair showing. Did one section let you down, or did you lose a few marks in each section?

18 to 25 A few aspects of the game need working on!

17 or below Afraid you need some all-round improvement before entering the big league!

60

ALL-ROUND EXPERT QUIZ

Neville Southall ➤

Everyone has a specialist position on the pitch when it comes to playing soccer . . . but what about soccer knowledge? This quiz is divided into FOUR parts – GOAL, DEFENCE, MID-FIELD and ATTACK. Check your score for each section and see if your total score is good enough to make you an ALL-ROUND EXPERT!

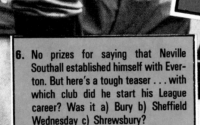

GOAL
Defence
Midfield
Attack

1. Which club did JIM LEIGHTON play for BEFORE he joined Manchester United?
   ANSWER _____

2. HOJN CULIK. Here's a top English 'keeper with his name all mixed up. Can you name him?
   ANSWER _____

3. Bruce Grobbelaar, Ray Clemence and Mike Hooper have all played for this great club. Which club?
   ANSWER _____

4. Name the celebrity. He's been playing League soccer for over 20 years and he's England's most capped 'keeper.
   ANSWER _____

5. What about the size of the goal that the 'keeper has to defend? F.A. rules state that the distance between the goal posts should be a) 8ft/2.44m b) 6yd/5.5m c) 8yd/7.32m. Which answer is correct?
   ANSWER _____

6. No prizes for saying that Neville Southall established himself with Everton. But here's a tough teaser . . . with which club did he start his League career? Was it a) Bury b) Sheffield Wednesday c) Shrewsbury?
   ANSWER _____

7. Pat Jennings was a great star during the 1960's, 70's and well into the 80's. In all he made 119 international appearances for his country between 1964 and 1986. But which country did Pat play for?
   ANSWER _____

8. True or false. Dave Beasant has saved a penalty-kick in a Wembley Final?
   ANSWER _____

9. Which country does the great Dassaev play for? Is it Iceland, France or Russia?
   ANSWER _____

10. Here are the last names of TWO 'keepers, but they're mixed together. SUPETTAONRS. Both goalies have the first name of Steve. Can you work out the names?
    ANSWER _____

11. PAT BONNER, IAN ANDREWS, PAUL COOPER and ALLEN McKNIGHT. Which 'keeper has NOT played for Celtic?
    ANSWER _____

12. Chris Woods of Rangers plays for Scotland. True or false?
    ANSWER _____

ANSWERS

1 Aberdeen, 2 John Lukic, 3 Liverpool, 4 Peter Shilton, 5 c, 6 a, 7 N.Ireland, 8 True, 9 Russia, 10 Sutton; Pears, 11 Paul Cooper, 12 False. He is an English international.

TOP SCORE 12
MY SCORE _____

ALL-ROUND EXPERT QUIZ

Steve Bould

GOAL
Defence
Midfield
Attack

1. **RKMA THIRGW.** It's a mixed up name of an England centre-half. Can you name him?
   ANSWER _____

2. **MICK McCARTHY, CHRIS HUGHTON** and **MARK MORRIS** all play for which country?
   ANSWER _____

3. Who is he? He started his career with Ipswich, then moved to Glasgow Rangers. He's a tough tackling, powerful defender who has made the centre-half position his own for England.
   ANSWER _____

4. **RICHARD GOUGH, GRAHAM ROBERTS** and **PAUL MILLER** have all played for this London team. Which team?
   ANSWER _____

5. **ALVIN _____ KEOWN** WHAT name is the LAST name of one centre-half and also the FIRST name of another centre-half?
   ANSWER _____

6. Willie Miller and Alex McLeish have played in a defensive partnership for both Aberdeen and Scotland. True or false?
   ANSWER _____

7. Which club did Steve Bould play for BEFORE he joined Arsenal?
   ANSWER _____

8. Gale of West Ham and Mowbray of Middlesbrough share the same first name. What is it?
   ANSWER _____

9. Which country did full-backs Mick Mills and Kenny Sansom play for?
   ANSWER _____

10. Brian Kilcline was a centre-half skipper for an F.A. Cup winning side. Was it Coventry, Liverpool or Wimbledon?
    ANSWER _____

11. Snodin, Ratcliffe, Watson, Van Den Hauwe. Which club have lined up with those back four players?
    ANSWER _____

12. Who is he? He started with Partick Thistle. He's been part of the Liverpool set up for over ten years. A centre-half, he became skipper of the Anfield team.
    ANSWER _____

ANSWERS

1 Mark Wright, 2 Republic of Ireland, 3 Terry Butcher, 4 Spurs, 5 Martin, 6 True, 7 Stoke, 8 Tony, 9 England, 10 Coventry, 11 Everton, 12 Alan Hansen.

TOP SCORE 12
MY SCORE _____

62

ALL-ROUND EXPERT QUIZ

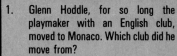

Jan Molby ➤

1. Glenn Hoddle, for so long the playmaker with an English club, moved to Monaco. Which club did he move from?
   ANSWER _____

2. Ronnie Whelan and Ray Houghton were team mates with the Republic of Ireland. With which club side did they also play together?
   ANSWER _____

3. ANJ BOYLM. Midfield mix-up. Sort out this player's name.
   ANSWER _____

4. Who am I? I started at West Brom, then Ron Atkinson took me to Old Trafford. I'm their skipper and I've become the skipper of England.
   ANSWER _____

5. Which country did the great Michel Platini play for? Was it Belgium, France or Holland?
   ANSWER _____

6. Chelsea, Man Utd, A C Milan, Paris St Germain, Rangers. One former England midfielder has played for ALL these clubs. Can you name him?
   ANSWER _____

7. Who moved from Newcastle to Spurs in a much publicised £2 million transfer in 1988? Was it Terry Fenwick, Paul Gascoigne, or Gary Stevens?
   ANSWER _____

8. What's the first name shared by both Hodge and McMahon?
   ANSWER _____

9. Can anyone remember a Celtic side without Roy Aitken? But, in fact, Roy had played for two other League sides before he went to Celtic. Is that true or false?
   ANSWER _____

10. 'Bracewell lays the ball out to Trevor Steven who pushes a short pass to McCall . . .' Which side fielded these midfielders?
    ANSWER _____

11. Which tough midfielder proved himself an equally tough manager when he became player/manager with Rangers, and won the Premier title in his first season?
    ANSWER _____

12. Which club has Jim Bett NOT played for: ABERDEEN, AIRDRIEONIANS, RANGERS and SUNDERLAND?

ANSWERS

1. Spurs, 2 Liverpool, 3 Jan Molby, 4 Bryan Robson, 5 France, 6 Ray Wilkins, 7 Paul Gascoigne, 8 Steve, 9 False, 10 Everton, 11 Graeme Souness, 12 Sunderland.

TOP SCORE 12

MY SCORE ___

ACTION EXTRA

John Sheridan
Sheffield Wednesday

John Sheridan, the former
Leeds star, joined
Nottingham Forest in
1989...but moved to
Sheffield Wednesday a few
months later without
playing a League game for
Brian Clough's team!

Back Up Front!

They score goals as well as stopping them!

Ian Rush, John Aldridge, Brian McClair, Tommy Coyne, Marco van Basten, Gary Lineker, Ally McCoist. What do these players have in common? They're all hot-shots . . . forwards whose business it is to find the net regularly. Bang! It's another one! The crowd roars!

STEVE FOSTER

DEREK MOUNTFIELD

But it's not only these well known front-runners and other similar performers who like to see their names on the scoresheet. Full-backs and central defenders love to get up into the opposing six-yard box, seeking a bit of glory for themselves. Their success rate makes impressive reading.

When Everton won the title in 1985, DEREK MOUNTFIELD weighed in

Back Up

with no less than 10 of their goals. Now he's with Aston Villa, linking up with another player whose forward surges have reaped reward in the past . . . ALLAN EVANS!

In April '86, Liverpool blasted Birmingham City 5-0 at Anfield. Grabbing a hat-trick for himself that day was central defender, GARY GILLESPIE. Not to be out-done, team-mate STEVE NICOL – playing at right-back – knocked the stuffing out of Newcastle at St. James' Park in September '87 with three in a 4-1 victory that told Tyneside who were the tops.

ALVIN MARTIN

Helping to prop up Black-burn's rearguard in season '87-'88 was CHRIS PRICE (now Villa) and COLIN HENDRY. Both reached double figures and helped Rovers to reach a Second Division play-off spot.

Luton skipper STEVE FOSTER will often help The Hatters with a timely goal or two, but he's yet to match the feat of fellow centre-half at West Ham, ALVIN MARTIN. On the run-in to the climax of the 1985/86 season, United hammered Newcastle at Upton Park and Martin hit a hat-trick in an 8-1 mauling of The Magpies.

Middlesbrough's suc-cessful skipper, TONY MOWBRAY, earned his club extra-time in a 1988 F.A. Cup Fourth Round replay versus Everton at Ayresome Park, with an equaliser in the dying seconds. The tie even-tually went to another game, but the hero suddenly turned villain! With the score level at 1-1, Tony turned the ball into his own net and booted Boro out of the competition!

The first Rous Cup was won by Scotland. They beat the "auld enemy" England 1-0 at Hampden thanks to a RICHARD GOUGH second-half header.

KEVIN MORAN has scored important goals for Man-chester United and the Republic Of Ireland, and PSV Eindhoven and Holland's RONALD KOEMAN likes nothing better than to try his luck at goal.

STEVE NICOL

Front!

TONY MOWBRAY

KEVIN MORAN

On March 20th, 1976, CHRIS NICHOLL (now manager at Southampton) was playing centre-half for Villa at home to Leicester. He got both his side's goals in a 2-2 draw. Unfortunately for him and his team-mates, he also netted both City's goals! He's earned himself a place in the record books, but no fellow back-four star will be in a hurry to equal that achievement!

They are the Top of the Scots...players who thrill supporters North of the Border with their wide range of skills. And, as you will see, these "Scottish" stars come from many different countries...such as Celtic's Polish forward Dariusz Dziekanowski (below).

TOP TEN

John Robertson, the talented Hearts striker

ABOVE
Motherwell's tricky winger Davie Cooper, who has also played for Clydebank and Rangers.

LEFT
Aberdeen's popular Dutch goalkeeper, Theo Snelders, who joined the Dons from FC Twente in 1988.

RIGHT
Jimmy Nicholl, Dunfermline's Northern Ireland international who has played club football in England, Canada and, of course, Scotland.

LEFT
Ally McCoist, the prolific Glasgow Rangers striker, began his career with humble St Johnstone in 1978 before joining Sunderland. He scored only eight goals in two seasons at Roker Park but since returning to Scotland with Rangers, it's been goals all the way for Super Ally.

ABOVE
Dundee full-back Arthur Albiston had a successful career in England with Manchester United and West Brom. He moved to Dens Park in 1989.

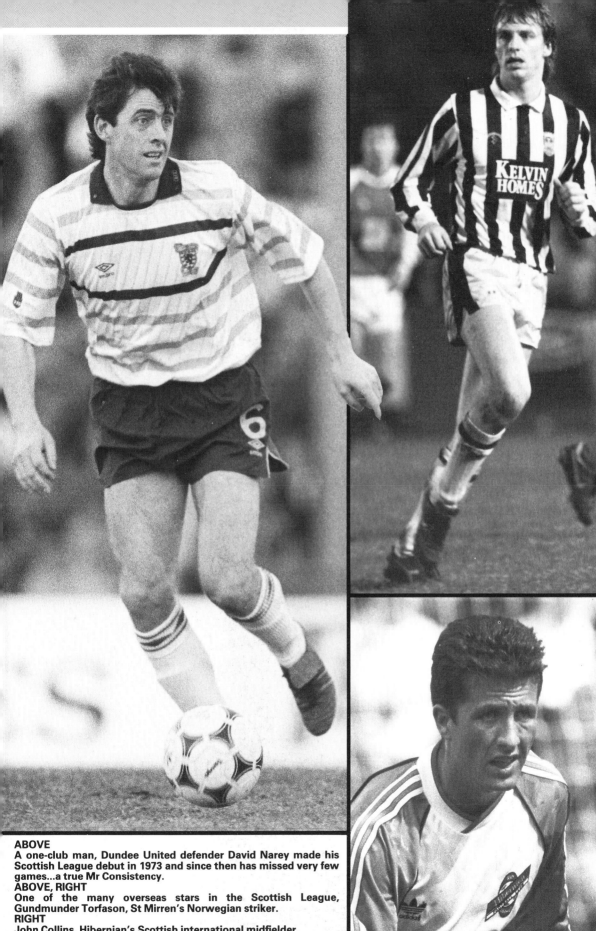

ABOVE
A one-club man, Dundee United defender David Narey made his Scottish League debut in 1973 and since then has missed very few games...a true Mr Consistency.
ABOVE, RIGHT
One of the many overseas stars in the Scottish League, Gundmunder Torfason, St Mirren's Norwegian striker.
RIGHT
John Collins, Hibernian's Scottish international midfielder.

STARS OF THI

Two sizzling Saints...at the top
of the page Southampton
winger Rod Wallace beats two
Arsenal defenders while, above,
brother Ray, a full-back, is
another promising member of
the football family.

I have to smile when people
say that the stars of today
aren't as good as the stars
of yesterday. I believe the
present day players are not
only as good but in many cases
BETTER than their
predecessors.

I am optimistic that the Nineties
will not only see a bumper crop of
young stars coming through but
that English clubs will once again
dominate Europe.

Remember, before the UEFA
ban in 1985 English clubs
invariably won at least one of the
three Euro Cups each year and I
see no reason why that situation
should not be repeated again
soon.

So who will be the big names
of tomorrow?

Bryan Robson has been a huge
influence on English football,
both for Manchester United and
England and perhaps Paul Ince,
who joined the Reds from West
Ham in 1989, can one day be as
effective.

Bryan didn't really become a
household name until he was
about 23 – his career with West
Bromwich Albion was held back
by three leg-breaks.

Paul didn't have the easiest of
times when he went to United
but he may look back on the
period as character building.

You need to experience bad
times to appreciate the good
times and amid the Old Trafford
problems Paul showed his class
both in midfield and at right back.

My guess is that it will be in
midfield, in a similar role to that
of Bryan, that Paul will eventually
make his mark in a big way.

90'S

Southampton's Matthew Le Tissier (above) and Arsenal striker Paul Merson – great goalscorers.

Paul has the same dynamic style as Bryan and playing alongside the United captain can only help the youngster.

Danny Wallace joined United from Southampton at roughly the same time as Paul but down at the Dell the Saints fans joke that Alex Ferguson signed the wrong Wallace.

On the South Coast they reckon that brother Rodney, like Danny a speedy winger, is a better prospect and certainly Rodney has enormous potential.

He is probably a better finisher than Danny and in 1989/90, his first full season in Division One, reached double figures in the goal charts by Christmas.

Rodney is as fast as a racehorse and that, coupled with excellent ball control and an eye for goal, makes Wallace junior one of the best prospects in the League.

I must not forget another Saint called Wallace – Ray Wallace – who, unlike his brothers, is a defender but has the same pace that seems to be the family's hallmark.

Another good prospect at the Dell is Matthew Le Tissier, their winger born in the Channel Islands.

Matthew scores a lot of goals and his combination with Rodney Wallace gives Southampton possibly the best pair of wingers in Division One.

Arsenal have one of the most productive youth policies in the League and have unearthed a stream of promising youngsters...Frank Stapleton, Liam Brady, David O'Leary and others...over the years.

I like the look of Paul Merson, their powerful striker who forced his way into England's Under-21

ABOVE
Whatever else Michael Thomas achieves in his career, he will always be remembered as the player who scored the goal at Liverpool that won the 1989 League title for Arsenal.
ABOVE, RIGHT
David Howells, Tottenham's Guildford-born midfielder is a former England Youth international.
RIGHT
Paul Gascoigne (white shirt) of Tottenham gets to grips with Andy Townsend, Norwich's Republic of Ireland midfielder.

Dalian Atkinson, the dangerous Sheffield Wednesday stiker.

team in 1988/89 as he helped the Gunners win the Championship.

Arsenal loaned Paul to Brentford for a spell while he learnt his trade and after completing his apprenticeship in the reserves and lower divisions, he showed just what a good centre-forward he is.

Another youngster – although a household name – at Highbury is Michael Thomas, who put his name in the history books by scoring the dramatic last minute goal at Liverpool in May, 1989, that clinched the title.

Like Paul, Michael was loaned out by Arsenal to give him valuable experience – to Portsmouth – but he is now one of the most complete players in the top flight.

Michael generally plays in midfield but is effective at right-back, too. Playing in the centre of the park, he times his runs into opponents' penalty areas perfectly – as his goal at Anfield proved.

A few miles away at Tottenham there is one of the biggest personalities in the League – Paul Gascoigne.

Gazza made his name with Newcastle before Terry Venables bought him for £2 million and while some critics have doubts about Paul, in my book he is the sort of player all supporters love to watch.

He can do the most incredible things with the ball – getting out of a tight situation which even Houdini would have found difficult! And Gazza has shown on many occasions his ability to score a goal when no goal seems posssible.

Paul Lake of Manchester City...seen here in action for the England Under-21 side.

ABOVE...Paul Williams scored some valuable goals for Charlton last season.
BELOW...Roy Wegerle, QPR's £1 million striker signed from Luton.
RIGHT...Ipswich's versatile Jason Dozzell, an England Under-21 star.

Gary "Bing" Crosby, the Nottingham Forest winger who can play either on the right or the left wing.

Another Spurs youngster who made his mark in 1989/90 is David Howells, whose performances in midfield were often of the highest class.

Manchester City have some of the most promising young players in the League and Howard Kendall is the ideal manager to bring out their potential.

Paul Lake is a solid full-back, Liverpool-born centre-back Steve Redmond reacted positively to the responsibility of being captain, while David White is a winger with an eye for goals.

Paul Williams didn't have the easiest of introductions to the First Division with Charlton, who always seem to be battling against relegation.

However, the striker showed a maturity beyond his years in a struggling side with some important goals.

Jason Dozzell has had seven years' experience in the League with Ipswich but he's still only in his early 20's and the next few seasons should see him really make a name for himself.

Young Gary Crosby has made a name for himself on Nottingham Forest's right wing over the past couple of seasons.

Gary began his career with Lincoln but drifted out of the Football League to play for Grantham until Brian Clough snapped him up for a bargain fee in 1987.

The name of Atkinson at Sheffield Wednesday originally conjured up thoughts of Big Ron, the Hillsborough boss.

These days the distinction of being Wednesday's star Atkinson is shared by striker Dalian, no relation, a big bustling striker bought from Ipswich in 1989.

Roy Wegerle is another entertainer who must succeed during the coming decade. Moving from Luton to QPR in a seven-figure deal at the end of 1989, he was soon delighting the fans. Keep an eye on him!

I would need almost the entire annual to tell you about all the youngsters who could make it to the top during the Nineties.

The ones I've spoken about are just a few of the bright young lads who have a big future in front of them.

ACTION EXTRA

Ian Wright
Crystal Palace

Ian Wright, the Crystal Palace goal machine, can do no wrong in the eyes of the Selhurst Park supporters who idolise the Eagles' striker.

HAMISH and MOUSE

HOT-SHOT HAMISH BALFOUR AND KEVIN 'MIGHTY' MOUSE PLAYED FOR PRINCES PARK FC IN THE SCOTTISH PREMIER DIVISION, AND MIGHTY MOUSE ALSO WORKED AT ST DUNCAN'S HOSPITAL...

X'MAS FOOTER FOR CHARITY!
St Duncan's Hospital
V
Princes Park F.C.
WEDNESDAY K O 2·30

WELL, MOUSE — YOU'RE SUPPOSED TO HAVE TRAINED THE HOSPITAL TEAM. ARE THEY UP TO *WORLD CUP* STANDARD FOR SKILL AND FITNESS?

YOU'RE *JOKING*, MATRON! THAT BUNCH OF BANANAS HAVEN'T GOT *ANY* SKILL!

HOSPITAL

THEY'RE NOT *FIT*, EITHER! IF THEY PLAYED *LUDO* THEY'D ALL GET OUT OF BREATH!

WELL, THERE'S TWO DAYS BEFORE THE GAME. IF ST DUNCAN'S *LOSE*...

I KNOW! I'LL BE *FIRED*!

CORRECT!

ON THE *OTHER* HAND, IF YOU GET THE HOSPITAL TEAM TO *WIN*...YOU'LL BE *PROMOTED* TO THE NEW EMERGENCY RESCUE SERVICE!

THAT SOUNDS BETTER!

82

CAPTAIN FANTASTIC!

Bryan Robson suffered three broken leg setbacks when he was a youngster with West Bromwich Albion and although injuries have been unkind to Robbo, he has still emerged as the most influential player for Manchester United and England over the past 10 years. He is Captain Fantastic...Captain Marvel...Captain Courageous...he'll play in pain for club and country because they mean so much to him. England have already had one manager called Robson (Bobby), but one day Bryan may succeed his namesake in charge of the national team! You never know...

Robbo on top...as usual! Bryan jumps for this high ball during the friendly against Holland at Wembley in March, 1989, which ended 2–2.

CAPTAIN FANTASTIC!

Bryan led England to the 1990 World Cup Finals with some outstanding displays, such as the one against Poland at Wembley in June, 1989 (above) when England won 3–0. Here, Captain Marvel is seen challenging Poland's Krzysztof Warsycha. On the right...a familiar pose as Robbo shows the all-action style that has made him one of the greatest players ever to represent Manchester United.

TACKLING

Roy of the Rovers TEACH-IN

WINNING THE BALL

INCORRECT

CORRECT

TACKLING WITH THE TOE

TACKLING WITH THE SIDE OF THE FOOT

SLIDING TACKLE

TACKLING TO WIN THE BALL

When a defender makes a tackle he must get as close as possible to the man in possession. By getting in close he is able to tackle with the side of his foot giving him the largest possible area to drive through the ball and take it away from the attacker. This also applies to the player when making a sliding tackle.

DELAYING TACTICS

DELAYING TACTICS

When shadowing an attacker racing down the wing, delay your tackle so denying the attacker the choice of being able to beat you on the INSIDE or the OUTSIDE. Eventually the attacker will be trapped in a corner and this is your moment to get in a tackle for he can only go ONE WAY.

GOALKEEPING

Roy of the Rovers TEACH-IN

ONE AGAINST ONE

In a one against one situation the goalkeeper should get close enough to the forward so that he can't be lobbed; then spread himself, prepared to save with his feet, his body or his hands. This situation calls for skill and bravery.

ATTACK CENTRE AND CATCH AT THIS POINT

SIX-YARD BOX

Every nasty, swinging cross into the six-yard box is the goalkeeper's property and you must learn to come off your line and attack the ball, picking it cleanly out of the air. The secret of clean handling in these situations is the position of the thumbs – they must be placed directly behind the ball.

Every 'keeper should learn to think in terms of triangles – because every situation he faces is, in a sense, a triangle. Especially so when a forward has broken clean through – then the 'keeper has to run to meet the attacker as quickly as possible so reducing the BASE of the triangle – giving the forward less of the goal to shoot at. This means, quite simply, taking up the positions which will lessen the chances of a forward scoring and increase the chances of the 'keeper making the save.

DON'T STRETCH – STRIDE

When in possession and moving at top speed through a defence, use a shorter stride. The shorter stride gives better balance, which allows the player to control the ball better.

STRIDE

STRETCH

SHIELDING THE BALL

When running alongside the touchline, control the ball with the outside of the foot. Shielding the ball in this manner means the attacking player keeps his body between his opponent and the ball, which also means there is no way the player in possession can be tackled fairly.

INSTEP CONTROL

Controlling the ball with the instep is more difficult than controlling it with the INSIDE of the foot – because the area of contact with the ball is much SMALLER. But it is one which must be learnt because it allows you a more NATURAL RUNNING POSITION. Many top professionals have perfected this skill.

ROY of the ROVERS TEACH-IN

Roy of the Rovers TEACH-IN

CALLING FOR THE BALL

It is impossible for the player in possession to be aware of everything that is happening on the field of play. Notice how the professional players alert their team-mates with clear concise calls to situations happening outside their range of vision.

GOAL AREA

The goalkeeper is in the perfect position to see and advise on what is happening in and around the penalty box. When shouting instructions always use a team-mate's NAME to comply with the laws. Peter Shilton of Derby puts confidence in his defenders by always shouting in a loud and positive voice. In the diagram a defender chased by an attacker is covering a ball hit forward into the penalty area. It is now the goalkeeper's responsibility to shout, TOUCH IT – LEAVE IT – or 'KEEPER'S BALL.

'MY BALL!'

THE 'KEEPER MUST SHOUT – HE CAN SEE CLEARLY

OPPONENTS' PENALTY AREA

Notice how cleverly some players shield the ball from an opponent trying to tackle them from behind. In this situation, when you are in a supporting attacking position, DON'T SHOUT! Simply race forward into the penalty area, where your team-mate can pick you out with a pass. If you telegraph your movements to the defence they will pick you up. There is no need to shout to the man with the ball because he can see the space you are creating.

MIDFIELD

You should act as an extra pair of eyes when a team-mate, about to receive the ball, is threatened by a flying tackle from behind. Shout a warning that he must play it first time and knock the ball back into the space for him to run on to. Equally, a call of "hold it" will indicate when he is on his own in space, free from opponents.

MAN ON BALL IS IN CONTROL OF SITUATION

SKILLS

SPECIAL

Roy of the Rovers TEACH-IN

Many moments in football require a player to adapt his skills quickly. A hopeless situation can be turned to your advantage by a special skill.

KEEP KNEE WELL BACK

BODY LEVEL WITH GROUND

LENGTHEN STRIDE

OVERHEAD KICK

Practise the overhead kick whilst standing. Make contact with the full instep and keep your ankle firm with the toes pointing away, for the flight of the ball is governed by the position of the knee at impact. To perform a scissors kick, throw one leg in the air by thrusting upwards with the standing foot, then quickly bring that foot off the floor to actually kick the ball – remember to use your hands to break your fall.

THE BACKHEEL

The inside of the non-kicking foot is placed at the side of the ball – then feint, as if to kick the ball, but allow your kicking foot to move over and forward of the ball – you then backheel it to a team-mate in support behind you. This requires extreme accuracy of contact – the heel bone is very narrow – unless contact is made exactly dead centre, the ball will screw astray.

STEPPING OVER THE BALL

When racing forward to receive a pass in a crowded penalty area you can wrong-foot a defence by shaping as if to collect the ball but then widening your stride, allowing it to pass through your legs to an unmarked team-mate moving up in support. The secret here is to keep running after you have sold the 'dummy' for this all adds to the deception and confusion.

HEEL BONE MAKES CONTACT DEAD CENTRE OF THE BALL

DEFENSIVE TACTICS

ROY of the ROVERS TEACH-IN

In diagram A the defender has left his defence open to a through ball because he is close marking the opposition forward.

In diagram B the defender has intelligently placed himself in a position to intercept either a pass to the attacker or a through ball through the middle.

A

DEFENDER

B

DEFENDER

OVERLAP DOWN THE WING

The hopeful forward cross is a waste of time diagram A – for the attackers have their backs goal and the defenders have the simple job running forward to clear the ball.

In diagram B the attacking defender shows th advantage of pulling the ball back from the dea ball line. The attackers are now facing the ball an they can run forward to meet the cross which moving away from the defenders.

TACKLING

A

WEIGHT FORWARD

B

Release pressure and lift the ball over opponent's foot

C

Weight on back foot

When the defender moves into the tackle – diagram A – he keeps his weight well forward. This allows a quicker recovery because his weight is on his toes.

When two opposing players go into a tackle with equal determination – diagram B – there are times when the ball gets trapped between their feet. On occasions like this, you should release the pressure slightly and scoop the ball over your opponent's foot. The defender who sticks out a foot – diagram C – and tackles half-heartedly out of range, is hopelessly off balance and unable to turn quickly if beaten.

A

FORWARDS' BACKS' TO GOAL

B

DEFENDER

FORWARDS FACING GOAL

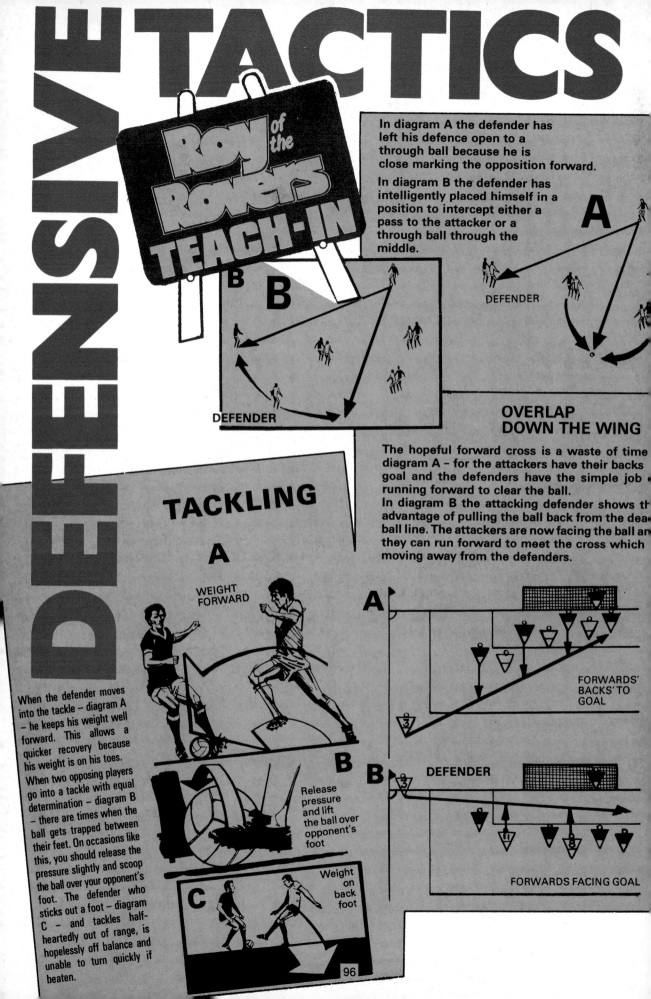

He may have a Cockney accent, but Norwich City's all-action midfield star Andy Townsend is proud to play for the Republic of Ireland.

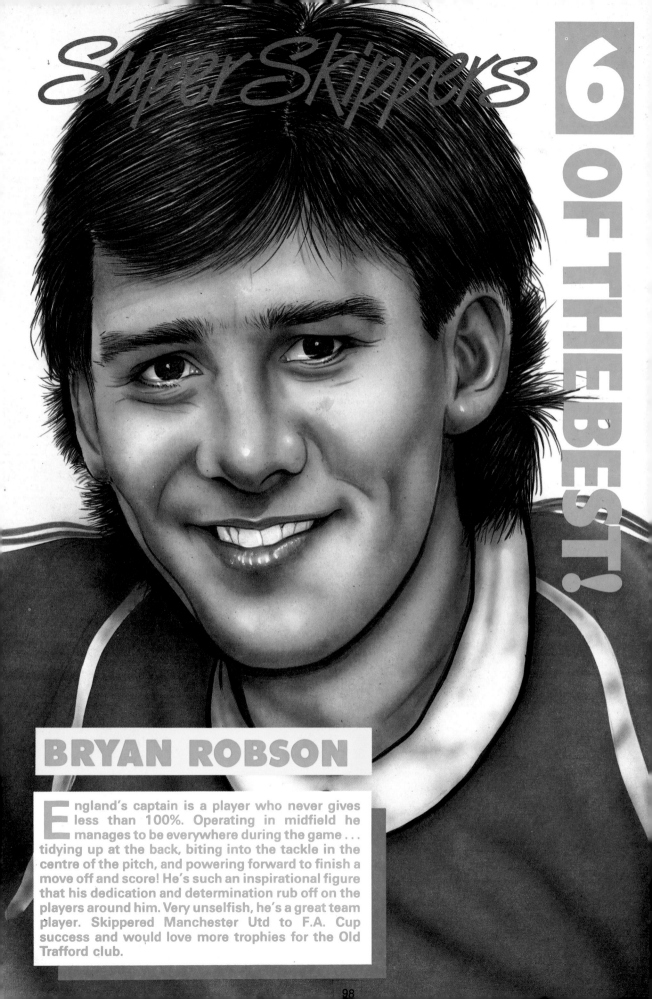

BRYAN ROBSON

England's captain is a player who never gives less than 100%. Operating in midfield he manages to be everywhere during the game . . . tidying up at the back, biting into the tackle in the centre of the pitch, and powering forward to finish a move off and score! He's such an inspirational figure that his dedication and determination rub off on the players around him. Very unselfish, he's a great team player. Skippered Manchester Utd to F.A. Cup success and would love more trophies for the Old Trafford club.

ROY AITKEN

Long established as a vital part of Celtic's midfield, Roy is a tough, gritty competitor, who loves to be involved in the game. He seems to thrive on the responsibility of being captain of his side, and is firmly in control of the players in his charge. Throughout the game he's directing operations, instructing people about their positional play and always demanding that extra bit of effort. His own non-stop game and commanding personality are a constant reminder for his team-mates to produce their best form.

ALAN HANSEN

The Scottish centre-half has steered Liverpool to some great triumphs, including the amazing Double of League and F.A. Cup in 1986. It's no secret that The Reds have a superb backroom staff who make sure that every player knows what he has to do out on the pitch. But someone has to be there on match day, making sure that things go according to plan . . . and that man is Hansen. As a player he's calm and unhurried, and he provides a steadying influence when the play gets too fast and frantic.

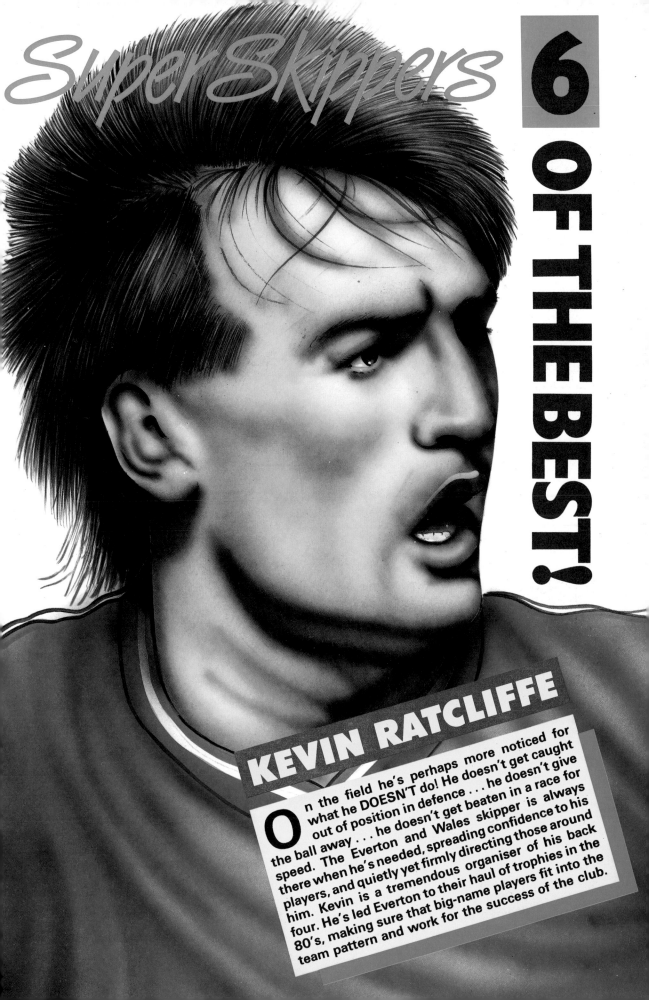

OF THE BEST!

KEVIN RATCLIFFE

O n the field he's perhaps more noticed for what he DOESN'T do! He doesn't get caught out of position in defence . . . he doesn't give the ball away . . . he doesn't get beaten in a race for speed. The Everton and Wales skipper is always there when he's needed, spreading confidence to his players, and quietly yet firmly directing those around him. Kevin is a tremendous organiser of his back four. He's led Everton to their haul of trophies in the 80's, making sure that big-name players fit into the team pattern and work for the success of the club.

RUUD GULLIT

Gullit's finest hour as a skipper came when he led the multi-talented Dutch side to triumph in the 1988 European Championship. The Dutch team need very little organising on the pitch, and all their players are technically equipped to play themselves out of trouble. Sometimes they need that extra spark to make things happen . . . and that's where Ruud shows why he's skipper of the side. A piece of individual genius, a measured pass to a team mate, a lightning dash into the penalty area and WHAM! another great Gullit goal.

DIEGO MARADONA

He was the captain who held aloft the World Cup in 1986 after he had led Argentina to victory. Maradona is a superstar player, a man who can win any game with a split second of attacking genius. His own skills enable him to lead solo charges where he is willing to take on any number of defenders and still go for a goal. But as a skipper Maradona is aware of his responsibilities to his team mates, and his ability to hold on to the ball and make space for others was a big factor in the Argentinian triumph.

BUT ANDY STEEL—AT FIFTEEN, THE YOUNGEST PLAYER IN ENGLISH LEAGUE FOOTBALL—WENT RELENTLESSLY ON ...

MIKE..!

ON MY WAY, ANDY ...

A BEAUTIFUL CHIP OVER THE UNITED DEFENCE ...

MIKE MALONE'S GONE BEHIND THEM. HE WAS JUST WAITING FOR THE CHIP ..!

YEESSS! IT'S A GOAL!

GREAT HEADER! ONE-NIL!

A BRILLIANT SET PIECE BY MILLSIDE!

IT WAS ONLY THE START. THE YOUNG PLAYMAKER STARTED TO RUN RIOT...

THAT'S IT, ANDY, MY SON! TAKE 'EM TO THE CLEANERS!

I'VE SEEN THE BOY HAVE SOME GOOD GAMES, BILL—BUT HE'S REALLY ON-SONG TODAY!

BILL STEEL, FOSTER FATHER AND ASSISTANT COACH, WATCHED WITH SATISFACTION ...

AYE, JERRY. THE LAD'S BLESSED WITH THE SORT OF NATURAL TALENT YOU DON'T SEE OFTEN. WHEN HE TICKS THE WHOLE TEAM TICKS. JUST LIKE A WELL-OILED MACHINE ...

YOUNG ANDY STEEL IN MIDFIELD HAS GOT AMAZING SKILLS ON THE BALL. THE SORT THAT HAVE CROWDS APPLYING FOR IDENTITY CARDS AND FLOCKING THROUGH THE GATES. NO WONDER THEY CALL HIM THE PLAYMAKER!

LATER, IN THE DRESSING-ROOM...

YOU'VE SHOWERED FAST, SON. WHAT'S THE HURRY?

THEY'VE ASKED ME TO LAUNCH A NEW SOCCER GAME, SKIPPER. IT WAS THE ONLY TIME I COULD FIT IT IN!

PLAYERS AND OFFICIALS ONLY

HERE HE COMES!

OOOOH! HE'S NICE!

GET HIS AUTOGRAPH!

MINE, TOO, PLEASE, ANDY!

CAN YOU WRITE A MESSAGE AS WELL?

BUT, AT LAST...

PHEW, THANKS, UNCLE BILL. THAT WAS WORSE THAN SOME OF THE TACKLES THAT WERE FLYING ABOUT ON THE PITCH TODAY!

IT'S ALL PART OF BEING A FAMOUS FOOTBALLER, ANDY!

PLAYMAKER THE SOCCER GAME OF THE 90's! NEW! EXCITING! SKILFUL!

AND NOW, LADIES AND GENTLEMEN, PLEASE MEET OUR GUEST OF HONOUR, ANDY STEEL OF MILLSIDE CITY AND ENGLAND UNDER-21'S...

PLAYMAKER THE SOCCER GAME OF THE 90's!

ANDY REPRESENTED THE PERFECT IMAGE OF FOOTBALL. THE OFFERS CAME IN THICK AND FAST...

WE'D LIKE ANDY TO GIVE HIS NAME TO A CHOCOLATE BAR, MR. STEEL... CALLED *PLAYMAKER*...!

EDITOR

OUR MAGAZINE *NEEDS* ANDY. OUR READERS ARE INTERESTED IN HIS VIEWS AND OPINIONS OF THE GAME...

FINALLY, THE MOST POWERFUL MEDIUM OF ALL...*TELEVISION!*

SPORTING CHALLENGE

ANDY STEEL

NOW ONE FOR YOU, ANDY. LIVERPOOL JUST FAILED TO BEAT THE RECORD RUN FOR AN UNBEATEN START TO A SEASON IN 1987/8. FOR TWO POINTS, WHAT HAPPENED?

THEY WENT 29 GAMES AND EQUALLED LEEDS UNITED'S UNBEATEN RECORD IN 1974.

CORRECT!

BOTH ANDY AND BILL STEEL WERE POWERLESS TO CONTROL THE MEDIA MACHINE...

...THE PLAYMAKER'S FACE WAS EVERYWHERE!

SUNDAY SPO

"ANDY DECIDES THE MATCH

BE LIKE ME DON'T SMOKE

GOOD GRACIOUS! WHAT ARE ALL THOSE *GIRLS* DOING WAITING OUTSIDE THE SCHOOL GATES?

THEY'RE WAITING FOR *STEEL*, SIR!

HE'S THE CURRENT NUMBER ONE PIN-UP BOY!

IS THIS ACTUALLY *TRUE*, STEEL?

ER...I'M AFRAID SO, SIR. IT'S NOT MY FAULT...

ANDY, CAN YOU RUN DOWN TO THE SHOPS FOR ME? I'VE RUN OUT OF PEPPER...

IT'S A BIT DIFFICULT, AUNT MARGARET. I GET MOBBED WHEREVER I GO...

...AND THEY'RE LYING IN WAIT FOR ME NOW!

AND THEN...

ANDY...YOU'VE BEEN INVITED TO PLAY IN A TESTIMONIAL MATCH FOR JEFF HUNTER, WHO'S HAVING TO GIVE UP THE GAME...

THE *ENGLAND* PLAYER-?

YES. AND IT'LL BE ONE OF THE MOST STAR-STUDDED OCCASIONS FOR YEARS. EVERY LEADING PLAYER IN EUROPE WILL BE THERE. IT'S A REAL HONOUR THAT YOU'VE BEEN ASKED.